Goose at the Beach

by Laura Wall

AWARD PUBLICATIONS LIMITED

"Wake up, Goose!" says Sophie.

"The sun is shining. We're on holiday!"

"Today we're going to the beach!"

Goose has never been to the beach before.

Sophie and Mum pack their things
in a beach bag.

And they put on some sun screen.

When they get to the beach,
Sophie wiggles her toes in the warm sand.

And Goose discovers he can make footprints!

This gives Sophie an idea.

"Let's draw a picture in the sand!"

Goose finds some shells and seaweed to make it extra special.

"What a lovely picture!" says Sophie.

Goose and Sophie make sand angels.

Lots of them!

But wait, where is Goose?

Surprise!

Sophie and Goose are all sandy.

Mum suggests they wash it off in the water.

But Sophie isn't sure. The sea looks very big.

Goose takes her hand and they paddle together.

And jump in the waves.

"This is so much fun!" laughs Sophie.

Playing in the water has made
their tummies rumble.

Sophie puts on her sun hat
while Mum gets the picnic ready.

Sophie and Goose eat their lunch.

But someone wants to share Goose's food!

OUCH! Poor Goose!

"Perhaps an ice cream will cheer you up,"
suggests Sophie.

"Yum!"

"Mmm!" smiles Sophie. "That was good!"

"Let's build a sandcastle!" says Sophie.

They set to work with their
buckets and spades.

Sophie wants theirs to be the
tallest on the beach.

And the prettiest.

But ... uh oh!

"Goose! Our sandcastle!" cries Sophie.

Goose is sad. Sophie is sad too.

Some children come to see what's wrong,
but Sophie can't understand them.

The boy smiles. Maybe he has an idea.

He starts to build a new sandcastle.

Soon more children come to help.

And together they build the biggest, most amazing sandcastle ever!

"What a beautiful sandcastle!" says Sophie.

"Honk!" says Goose.